Piano Exam Pieces

ABRSM Grade 6
Selected from the 2025 & 2026 syllabus

Name

Date of exam

MW00804554

Contents

Footnotes: Philippa Bunting & Richard Jones (RJ)

You can listen to professional recordings of all 48 pieces on the syllabus – from both this book and the complete lists. They're available to stream from Spotify, Apple Music, Amazon and other major platforms.

Search **ABRSM Piano Exam Pieces 2025 & 2026** for the official ABRSM album.

This book contains nine pieces from the Grade 6 syllabus, but there are many more!

We encourage you to explore the full repertoire lists to discover exciting pieces that inspire you, that you will enjoy learning, and that will allow you to perform to your full potential. You'll find the additional options on page 24.

You can play a mixture of pieces from this book and from the full lists – you just need to pick one from each of the lists A, B and C.

Editorial guidance

We have taken the pieces in this book from a variety of sources. Where appropriate, we have edited the pieces to help you prepare for your performance. Editorial additions are given in small print, in square brackets or, for slurs and ties, in the form ⌒. Details of other changes or suggestions are given in the footnotes. These editorial additions are for guidance only: you do not have to follow them in the exam.

First published in 2024 by ABRSM (Publishing) Ltd, a wholly owned subsidiary of ABRSM, 4 London Wall Place, London EC2Y 5AU, United Kingdom
© 2024 by The Associated Board of the Royal Schools of Music
Distributed worldwide by Oxford University Press

Unauthorised photocopying is illegal
All rights reserved. No part of this publication may be reproduced, recorded or transmitted in any form or by any means without the prior permission of the copyright owner.

Music origination by Julia Bovee
Cover by Andy Potts
Printed in England by Caligraving Ltd, Thetford, Norfolk, on materials from sustainable sources.
P16211

Invention No. 14 in B flat

BWV 785

Edited by Richard Jones

J. S. Bach
(1685–1750)

Bach's two-part Inventions and three-part Sinfonias were composed in 1722–3 when he was employed as Kapellmeister at the court of Cöthen (north of Leipzig). According to the title page of the autograph fair copy, these pieces were designed to foster good playing in two and three parts, to help students to invent and develop good musical ideas, and above all 'to arrive at a cantabile style of playing and acquire a strong foretaste for composition'.

The B flat Invention, selected here, is essentially monothematic, like most of the Inventions. It is based on a decorated broken-chord theme, which is immediately followed by its own inversion. The witty play on direct and inverted forms of the theme that ensues is one of the main sources of the piece's attractiveness. Dynamics are left to the player's discretion. RJ

Source: autograph fair copy, 1723, Staatsbibliothek zu Berlin, Preussischer Kulturbesitz, Mus.ms.Bach P610

© 1984 by The Associated Board of the Royal Schools of Music
Reproduced from J. S. Bach: *Inventions & Sinfonias*, BWV 772–801, edited by Richard Jones (ABRSM)

AB 4122

Sonata alla Scarlatti

Germaine Tailleferre
(1892–1983)

Germaine Tailleferre was at the heart of French artistic life as a member of Les Six – a group of composers that also featured Georges Auric, Louis Durey, Arthur Honegger, Darius Milhaud and Francis Poulenc. She was a prolific, popular and often-performed composer during her lifetime, working as a musician up to the last few days of her life.

This upbeat, optimistic neo-Baroque piece is in her typical crisp, clear style. It was influenced by her early study of the harpsichord, and is rhythmically regular, requiring a light touch and delicate, accurate playing throughout. Dynamics are left to the player's discretion, since there are none provided by the composer.

5

AB 4122

Spilleværket

No. 6 from *Humoreske-Bagateller*, Op. 11

Carl Nielsen
(1865–1931)

Allegretto scherzando [♩ = *c*.96]

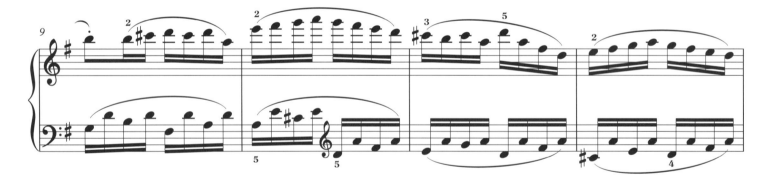

Danish composer Carl Nielsen was born in 1865, the seventh of 12 children in a rural family. His father was a house painter and traditional musician, and Nielsen drew on early experiences of village music-making to later build a career as a composer, conductor and violinist.

With its constantly restless semiquaver movement, this musical miniature evokes the intricate mechanism of a musical clock, all the parts fitting neatly and precisely together to create the magic of the final result.

Source: first edition, *Humoreske-Bagateller*, Op. 11 (Copenhagen & Leipzig: W. Hansen, 1897)

Bagatelle in F

No. 1 from Two Bagatelles

B:1

Fanny Hensel
(1805–47)

Born in Hamburg, Germany, Fanny Hensel (née Mendelssohn) was the older sister of Felix Mendelssohn. Despite prodigious musical ability, she was not encouraged to pursue music as a career due to the limiting social expectations of the time. In 1820, her father wrote in a letter: 'Music will perhaps become his [Felix's] profession, while for *you* it can and must be only an ornament.' Despite this, Fanny wrote 466 musical compositions before her early death.

This beautiful miniature, open and straightforward in mood, feels like chamber music, the inner parts contributing equally to the overall musical effect. Dynamics are left to the player's discretion, since there are none in the source.

Source: *Zwei Bagatellen für die Schüler des Schindelmeisser'schen Musik-Instituts* (Berlin: T. Trautwein'sche Buch- u. Musikalien-Handlung, n.d. [1848])

Sketch in D

Esquisse in D

No. 9 from *12 esquisses*, Op. 47

R. M. Glière
(1875–1956)

Reinhold Moritsevich Glière was born in Kiev (now Kyiv, Ukraine) and pursued his entire musical career within the territory of the then Soviet Union. During his time teaching at the Gnessin School of Music in Moscow, he gave piano lessons to both Nikolai Myaskovsky and also to an 11-year-old Sergey Prokofiev.

Glière composed four sets of 'esquisses' (sketches) of which this piece is drawn from the third. The soulful legato melody of the opening evokes the sonority of the cello and has a song-like quality. The middle section, heavily influenced by the 19th-century Russian romantic tradition, explores some more distant harmonies, before the melody reasserts itself at bar 35.

B:3

Last Song

from *The Secret Piano*

Alexis Ffrench
(born 1970)

Alexis Ffrench is a UK-based composer, producer and pianist. He says of this piece: 'Last Song was originally written for my daughter, Savannah, when she was a very young child, as a piece to accompany her early ballet dances. For me, it recalls the innocence of childhood and the wonder of possibility. I hope it resonates with you too as it becomes part of your story. Happy piano playing.'

The piece explores the singing quality of the piano and its expressive potential. Listen to what the inner parts contribute to the music, and explore the different tone colours suggested by the changing harmonies as you maintain the long legato lines.

Stamping Dance

No. 128 from *Mikrokosmos*, Vol. 5

Béla Bartók
(1881–1945)

This piece is taken from *Mikrokosmos* (from the Greek meaning 'little world'), a progressive series of pieces from those for beginners in book 1 to those at an advanced standard in books 5 and 6. The composer himself was the first person to perform pieces from *Mikrokosmos* in public, in London in 1937.

The music is informed by Bartók's immersive study of the folk music of Hungary, Romania, Algeria and Turkey, which is reflected in its angular tonality and complex dance-inspired rhythmic features. It is also a study in changing moods and tempi: think ahead to manage the transitions from one to another, releasing and controlling energy as the music dictates.

The Bounce

Zoe Rahman
(born 1971)

Zoe Rahman is a jazz pianist and composer of British Bengali and Irish heritage. She studied classical piano at the Royal Academy of Music, London, and Oxford University before winning a scholarship to study jazz performance at Berklee College of Music, Boston.

The 'bounce' of the title is reflected in the interesting syncopations, the bluesy feel further reinforced by the use of open fourths and fifths. It's a piece with attitude: angular and edgy, ranging across the keyboard with infectious drive.

Շուշիկի Šušiki

Shushiki

No. 4 from Dances

C:3

Komitas Vardapet
(1869–1935)

This piece, from Dances for Piano (Պարեր դաշնամուրի համար Parer dashnamuri hamar), draws on an original Armenian folk dance from Vagharshapat, typically for a solo female dancer, collected and arranged in the style of t'aṙ and dap'. The t'aṙ is a long-necked lute-like instrument with a distinctive double-bowled body, and the dap' is a relative of the tambourine.

There is a balance to find between the playful rhythmical patterns of the original šelody, the plucking of the t'aṙ and the beat of the dap', and the lyrical, sometimes impressionistic aspects of the piece. The composer's pedalling indications and expressive suggestions will guide you in finding the right tone for each phrase of this evocative dance. Although the composer's metronome mark is ♩. = 84, students may prefer a slower tempo, for example ♩. = c.66.

Sources: autograph MS, Komitas Museum–Institute, Yerevan, KA, No. 524–4; *Danses* (Paris: Maurice Senart, 1925). Performance directions are given in Armenian in the autograph manuscript but have been translated into English or Italian here.

Other pieces for Grade 6

		Composer	Piece	Publication
A	4	C. P. E. Bach	Solfeggietto in C minor, Wq.117/2	C. P. E. Bach: Selected Keyboard Works, Book 2 (ABRSM) *or* Classics to Moderns, Book 6 (Yorktown Music Press)
	5	J. S. Bach	Invention No. 6 in E, BWV 777	J. S. Bach: Two-part Inventions (ABRSM) *or* J. S. Bach: Inventions and Sinfonias (Henle)
	6	J. F. F. Burgmüller	Velocity, Op.109 No.10	J. F. F. Burgmüller: Studies, Op.109 (Peters)
	7	Cimarosa	Allegro (1st movt from *Sonata No. 6 in G*)	The Classical Spirit, Book 2 (Alfred)
	8	Handel	Fantasia in A	Classics to Moderns, Book 6 (Yorktown Music Press)
	9	Haydn	Finale: Allegro molto (4th movt from *Sonata in G*, Hob. XVI:6)	Haydn: Selected Keyboard Sonatas, Book 1 (ABRSM) *or* Haydn: Complete Piano Sonatas, Vol. 1 (Wiener Urtext)
	10	Hummel	Rondo in C, Op. 52 No. 6	Hummel: 16 Short Pieces (ABRSM)
	11	Knowles Paine	NEW Village Dance (No. 5 from *In the Country*, Op. 26)	Masters of American Piano Music (Alfred)
	12	Lindeman	NEW Allegretto (from *Character Pieces*)	Women Composers, Book 2 (Schott)
	13	B. Marcello	NEW Presto (2nd movt from *Sonata in G*)	A Keyboard Anthology, 3rd Series, Book 4 (ABRSM)
	14	D. Scarlatti	Sonata in A, Kp. 208, L. 238	D. Scarlatti: 200 Sonatas, Vol. 2 (EMB Zeneműkiadó)
	15	Schubert	Moment musical in F minor (No. 3 from *Moments musicaux*, D. 780)	Schubert: Moments musicaux, D. 780 (ABRSM) *or* Schubert: Impromptus and Moments musicaux (Henle)
	16	Telemann	Allegro (1st movt from *Fantasia No.1 in D*, 1st Dozen, TWV 33:1)	Telemann: Fantasias, 1st Dozen (ABRSM)
B	4	Albéniz	NEW Tango (No. 2 from *España*, Op.165)	Core Classics, Grades 5–6 (ABRSM)
	5	Mel Bonis	Interlude (from *Interlude et Valse lente*, Op. 38) *ending b. 53*	Mel Bonis: Piano Music Volume 5 – Dances A (Furore Verlag)
	6	Y. Bowen	A Pastel	Y. Bowen: A Pastel (Chester)
	7	Chopin	NEW Waltz in A minor, KK. IVb No.11 *with first repeat*	Chopin: Waltzes for Piano (Henle) *or* More Romantic Pieces for Piano, Book 4 (ABRSM)
	8	Dello Joio	Prayer of the Matador (No. 2 from *Lyric Pieces for the Young*)	The Boosey & Hawkes 20th-Century Piano Collection: from 1945 (Boosey & Hawkes)
	9	Glière	Prelude in D♭ (No.1 from *8 Easy Pieces*, Op. 43)	Glière: Eight Easy Pieces, Op. 43 (ABRSM) *or* A Romantic Sketchbook for Piano, Book 4 (ABRSM)
	10	Guastavino	Cantilena No.1 'Santa Fe para llorar' (from *10 Cantilenas Argentinas*)	Guastavino: 10 Cantilenas Argentinas (Melos)
	11	C. Hartmann	Nocturne	C. Hartmann: Two Piano Pieces (Edition HH)
	12	Stephen Hough	Little Lullaby (4th movt from *Suite R-B*)	Stephen Hough: Suite R-B and Other Enigmas (Weinberger)
	13	Howells	There Was a Most Beautiful Lady (No. 3 from *Country Pageant*)	Howells: Country Pageant & A Little Book of Dances (ABRSM) *or* Core Classics, Grades 5–6 (ABRSM)
	14	Khachaturian	Legend (No. 6 from *Pictures of Childhood*)	Khachaturian: Pictures of Childhood (Boosey & Hawkes)
	15	Schumann	Einsame Blumen (No. 3 from *Waldscenen*, Op. 82)	Schumann: Waldscenen, Op. 82 (ABRSM)
	16	Sam Wedgwood	NEW Empty Rooms (from *Sam Wedgwood's Project, Book 1*)	Sam Wedgwood's Project, Book 1 (EVC)
C	4	L. Bernstein	NEW Cool (from *West Side Story*), arr. Klose	Broadway Piano Solos (Boosey & Hawkes)
	5	L. Bernstein	For Stephen Sondheim (No. 3 from *13 Anniversaries*)	L. Bernstein: 13 Anniversaries (Boosey & Hawkes)
	6	Valerie Capers	NEW Mr "Satchmo" (from *Portraits in Jazz*)	Valerie Capers: Portraits in Jazz (OUP)
	7	Casella	Galop Final (No.11 from *11 Children's Pieces*, Op. 35)	Casella: 11 Children's Pieces (Universal)
	8	Ben Crosland	View from a Window (No.12 from *Cool Beans!*, Vol. 1)	Pp. 24–27 from Ben Crosland: Cool Beans!, Vol. 1 (Editions Musica Ferrum)
	9	Paul Harvey	Rumba Toccata	Paul Harvey: Rumba Toccata (Ricordi)
	10	Nikki Iles	East Coast Blues	Jazz on a Summer's Day (OUP)
	11	Mercury	NEW Somebody to Love, arr. Keveren	Queen for Classical Piano (Hal Leonard)
	12	Stephen Montague	Tsunami	Spectrum 2 (ABRSM)
	13	Prokofiev	Cortège de sauterelles (No. 7 from *Musiques d'enfants*, Op. 65)	Prokofiev: Musiques d'enfants, Op. 65 (Boosey & Hawkes)
	14	Nkeiru Okoye	Dancing Barefoot in the Rain (from *African Sketches*)	Piano Music of Africa and the African Diaspora, Vol. 1 (OUP)
	15	Poul Ruders	Shooting Stars	Spectrum 3 (ABRSM)
	16	Billy Taylor	I wish I knew how it would feel to be free, arr. Churchill	Nikki Iles and Friends, Book 1 (ABRSM)